# MY BIG FEELINGS

Sarah Read

Go here to get

**https://bookhip.com/HQWTBQ**

"The Anxious Monster" for FREE!

# THIS BOOK BELONGS TO

.......................................................................

.......................................................................

Matthew's feelings are a little like a deep blue sea.
Some days, they're calm — other days, they're as wild as can be.
It's hard to keep your head high and your feet on the ground
When things upset you and blow your feeling sea all around.

On Saturday, Matthew was with his mom and dad outside.
His parents took turns holding his bike as he learned to ride.
Matthew practiced very hard and he used all of his will.
He was ever so happy once he mastered the skill.

Matthew could finally ride his bike without falling down.
His tummy felt calm as he roared with laughter like a clown.
Those happy feelings were good but they didn't last all day.
When Matthew looked for a toy later, happiness went away.

Matthew felt knots in his tummy. He was an upset little boy
When he saw his sister playing with his favorite toy.
No matter what Matthew tried, Mia wouldn't let the toy go.
He asked nicely, then cried, stomped and pleaded — but Mia said "No!"

Dad took the toy from Mia when he saw that Matthew felt bad.
"Let's give this back to your brother," Dad said. "You can see that he's sad."
He then gave Matthew a hug — which made his anger float away.
Matthew felt so much better as he went off to play.

Later that night, Matthew lay wide awake in his bed.
He couldn't sleep; his mind roamed and he listened instead.
He heard the house creaking and many other sounds of the night.
He heard a noise he didn't recognize, and it gave him a fright.

Matthew's mind raced trying to match an image to the sound.
He tried to ignore it, but the more he tried, the more he found
Himself wide awake and scared. "I can't sleep alone," he said
As he made his way down the hall to Mom and Dad's bed.

He told them he'd heard something weird and felt scared and alone.
They stayed with him until he felt calm enough to be on his own.
"I'm proud of you for coming to tell us you felt scared," Mom said.
"You can tell us anything," Dad said as he tucked him into bed.

When Matthew was feeling tired and grumpy the following day,
He asked for help, and Mom helped make the grumpiness go away.
He can ask for help from Mom and Dad — Grandma and teachers too.
They'll all give him great ideas for how to feel less blue.

Sometimes, Matthew's family members just give him a cuddle.
When his feelings are all mixed up, cuddles help sort the muddle.
Mom found a quiet spot with a desk in the house for him too.
He spends time coloring — one of his favorite things to do.

Grandma bought him crayons and a book. She said coloring will
Give him something to focus on until his feelings are still.
Quiet time and coloring help get feelings to where they should be.
Matthew is happiest when there's calm water in his feeling sea.

# Thank you

What Did You Think of *My Big Feelings?*

Thank you for purchasing this book. I know you could have picked any number of books to read, but you picked this book and for that I am extremely grateful.

If you like the book... and if you'd be willing to spare just two or three minutes...would you be willing to share your review of the book on Amazon?

If you would, it would mean the absolute world to me!

Thank you SO much. This helps to get the book into as many hands as possible, helping other parents and educators!

I really appreciate all your support!

Sarah Read
children's book author

Go here to get

https://bookhip.com/HQWTBQ

"The Anxious Monster" for FREE!

Made in the USA
Las Vegas, NV
10 November 2023

80546638R00021